Key Stage 2

Number Patterns and Early Algebra

Steve Mills and Hilary Koll

Name _____

Schofield & Sims

Introduction

Recognising and understanding patterns is an important skill in mathematics which can be used in many ways. In this learning workbook you will find information about how to recognise, extend and explain number sequences, using and applying known number facts. You will also learn some simple algebra, which can be used to explain some of the patterns you find.

How to use this book

Before you start using this book, write your name in the name box on the first page.

Then decide how to begin. If you want a complete course on number patterns and early algebra, you should work right through the book from beginning to end. Another way to use the book is to dip into it when you want to find out about a particular topic. The contents page will help you to find the pages you need.

Whichever way you choose, don't try to do too much at once – it's better to work through the book in short bursts.

When you have found the topic you want to study, look out for these icons, which mark different parts of the text:

Activities

This icon shows you the activities that you should complete. You write your answers in the spaces provided. You might find it useful to have some scrap paper to work on for some of the activities. After you have worked through all the activities on the page, turn to pages A1 to A3 at the centre of the book to check your answers. When you are sure that you understand the topic, put a tick in the box beside it on the Contents page.

On pages 10 and 17, you will find **Progress Tests**. These contain questions that will check your understanding of the topics that you have worked through so far. Check your answers on page A4. It is important that you correct any mistakes before moving on to the next section.

At the back of the book you will find a **Final Test**. This will check your understanding of all the topics (page 26).

Explanation

This text explains the topic and gives examples. Make sure you read it before you start the activities.

Scrap Paper

This icon tells you when you may need to use scrap paper to work out your answers.

Fascinating Facts

This text gives you useful background information about the subject.

Contents

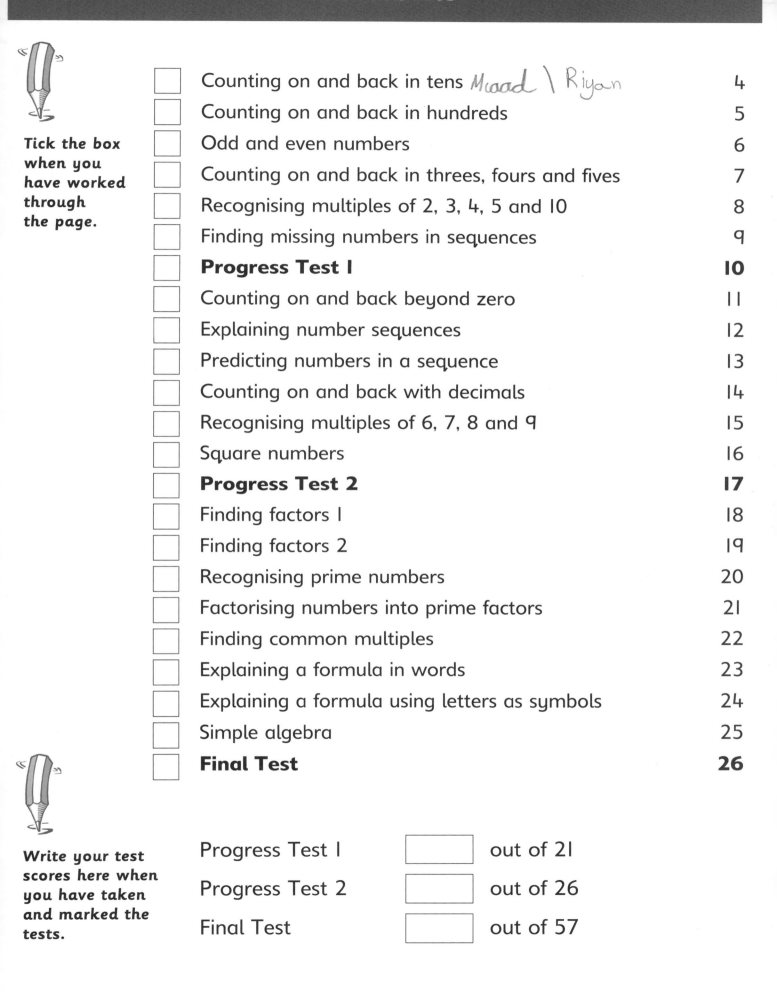

Tick the box when you have worked through the page.

Write your test scores here when you have taken and marked the tests.

Progress Test 1 ☐ out of 21

Progress Test 2 ☐ out of 26

Final Test ☐ out of 57

Counting on and back in tens

 **Did you know...?** A number sequence is a list of numbers arranged in a particular order and according to a rule. These are number sequences:

$$2, 4, 6, 8, 10 \ldots$$
↑
'add two'

$$1, 3, 9, 27, 81 \ldots$$
↑
'multiply by three'

Counting on and back in tens

Counting on and back in tens is easy because the unit digit stays the same.

Counting on in tens from 5

| 5 | 15 | 25 | 35 | 45 | 55 | 65 | 75 | 85 | 95 | 105... |

Counting back in tens from 127

| 127 | 117 | 107 | 97 | 87 | 77 | 67 | 57 | 47 | 37 | 27... |

 1. Count on in tens starting from:

a) 60 ___ ___ ___ ___ ___ ___ ___ ___ ___

b) 93 ___ ___ ___ ___ ___ ___ ___ ___ ___

 2. Count back in tens starting from:

a) 152 ___ ___ ___ ___ ___ ___ ___ ___

b) 218 ___ ___ ___ ___ ___ ___ ___ ___ ___

 3. Fill in the missing numbers in these sequences.

a) | | | 57 | 67 | 77 | | | | | |

b) | | | | | 123 | 133 | 143 | | |

c) | | 175 | | | | 135 | | |

d) | 368 | | | 328 | | | |

Counting on and back in hundreds

Counting on and back in hundreds

Counting on and back in hundreds is also easy because all the tens and unit digits stay the same.

Counting on in hundreds...

5   105   205   305   405   505   605   705   805   905   1005...

Counting back in hundreds...

1426   1326   1226   1126   1026   926   826   726...

1. Count on in hundreds starting from:

a) 300 _____ _____ _____ _____ _____ _____ _____ _____

b) 853 _____ _____ _____ _____ _____ _____ _____ _____

c) 1542 _____ _____ _____ _____ _____ _____ _____ _____

2. Count back in hundreds starting from:

a) 1400 _____ _____ _____ _____ _____ _____ _____ _____

b) 3782 _____ _____ _____ _____ _____ _____ _____ _____

c) 7861 _____ _____ _____ _____ _____ _____ _____ _____

3. Fill in the missing numbers in these sequences.

a)

	1100	1200			1500				

b)

				6617			6917		

c)

	5342				4942				

d)

			7551					7051	

e)

			8736	8836					

Odd and even numbers

Did you know... Every whole number is either **even** or **odd**.
Even numbers are whole numbers that can be divided exactly by **2** to give a whole number.

24 ÷ 2 = 12   so **24** is an **even** number

All numbers that end in **0**, **2**, **4**, **6** and **8** are **even** numbers.
These are **even** numbers:

6   18   54   270   832

Odd numbers are whole numbers that cannot be divided exactly by 2 to give a whole number.

25 ÷ 2 = 12 r 1   so **25** is an **odd** number

All numbers that end in **1**, **3**, **5**, **7** and **9** are **odd** numbers.
These are **odd** numbers:

3   15   67   121   659

1. Draw a ring around any **even** numbers you can see in this list.

23   56   78   109   814   157

2. Draw a ring around any **odd** numbers you can see in this list.

28   52   99   175   426   681

3. Give some examples to match these statements.

a) The numbers on both sides of an odd number are even.

6, 7, 8 and _____

b) The sum of three odd numbers is odd.

_____

c) The difference between any two even numbers or any two odd numbers is even.

_____

d) When two even numbers are multiplied the answer is even.

_____

Counting on and back in threes, fours and fives

Counting on and back in threes

Counting in threes means you are missing out two numbers each time...
Counting on in threes from **5** means you say '**five**, six, seven, **eight**, nine, ten, **eleven**...'

5   8   11   14   17   20   23   26   29   32   35...

1. a) Count on in threes from:

7 _____ _____ _____ _____ _____ _____ _____ _____ _____ _____

b) Count back in threes from:

58 _____ _____ _____ _____ _____ _____ _____ _____ _____ _____

Counting on and back in fours

Counting in fours means you are missing out three numbers each time...
Counting on in fours from **5** means you say '**five**, six, seven, eight, **nine**, ten...

5   9   13   17   21   25   29   33   37   41   45...

2. a) Count on in fours from:

7 _____ _____ _____ _____ _____ _____ _____ _____ _____ _____

b) Count back in fours from:

58 _____ _____ _____ _____ _____ _____ _____ _____ _____ _____

Counting on and back in fives

Counting in fives is easy because the unit digit repeats every other digit.

7   12   17   22   27   32   37   42   47   52   57...

3. a) Count on in fives from:

9 _____ _____ _____ _____ _____ _____ _____ _____ _____ _____

b) Count back in fives from:

83 _____ _____ _____ _____ _____ _____ _____ _____ _____ _____

Recognising multiples of 2, 3, 4, 5 and 10

 A **multiple** is a number that is in a times table or beyond.
Multiples of **4** are **4, 8, 12, 16, 20, 24, 28, 32, 36, 40, 44**... and they carry on in fours.
Multiples of **10** go up in tens and include **50, 60, 230** and **1690**.

 1. Write any five multiples of:

    a) 2 ___ ___ ___ ___ ___   **b) 3** ___ ___ ___ ___ ___

    c) 5 ___ ___ ___ ___ ___   **d) 8** ___ ___ ___ ___ ___

    e) 50 ___ ___ ___ ___ ___   **f) 100** ___ ___ ___ ___ ___

 2. Draw a ring around the numbers that are:

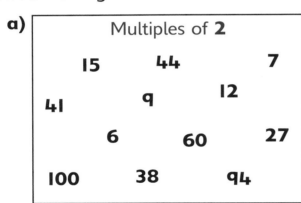

a) Multiples of **2**: 15, 44, 7, 41, 9, 12, 6, 60, 27, 100, 38, 94

b) Multiples of **3**: 25, 37, 9, 42, 18, 12, 15, 40, 27, 63, 39, 91

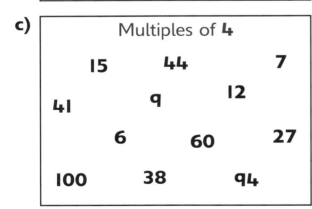

c) Multiples of **4**: 15, 44, 7, 41, 9, 12, 6, 60, 27, 100, 38, 94

d) Multiples of **5**: 25, 37, 9, 42, 18, 12, 15, 40, 27, 63, 39, 91

 **3.** Use the key to draw the correct shapes around the numbers.

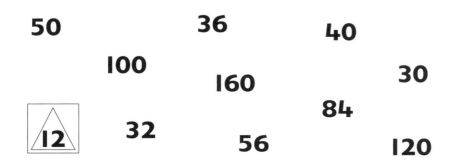

50   36   40
100   160   30
84
12   32   56   120

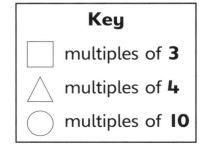

Key

☐ multiples of **3**
△ multiples of **4**
○ multiples of **10**

Finding missing numbers in sequences

Finding missing numbers in sequences

Sometimes you are asked to fill the gaps in sequences where you don't know the steps you are counting in, like this:

Fill in the missing numbers in this sequence:

6 21

To help you solve this: first look at this sequence:

4   6   8   10   12   14

2   2   2   2   2

Imagine you had been given just the first and last numbers:

4 14

The difference between **4** and **14** is **10**. Now count the **gaps** between **4** and **14**. There are **5** gaps. **10 ÷ 5 = 2** so each number is **2** more than the one before it. Now use this method for the question above.

6 21

The difference between **6** and **21** is **15**. There are **5** gaps (not **4** missing numbers). **15 ÷ 5 = 3** so each number is **3** more than the one before it.

6   9   12   15   18   21

1. Fill in the missing numbers in these sequences.

a) 9 ___ ___ ___ ___ 29   b) 12 ___ ___ ___ ___ 37

c) 17 ___ ___ ___ ___ 47   d) 19 ___ ___ ___ ___ 54

e) 154 ___ ___ ___ ___ 99   f) 207 ___ ___ ___ ___ 147

2. Fill in the missing numbers in these sequences.

a)

		45			57		

b)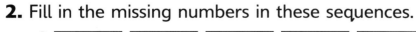

	73					38	

c)

			101				185

Progress Test I

1. Count on in tens starting from:

78 ___ ___ ___ ___ ___ ___

2. Fill in the missing numbers in this sequence.

| | | | | | 116 | 106 | 96 | | |

3. Count on in hundreds starting from:

294 ___ ___ ___ ___ ___ ___ ___ ___

4. Count back in hundreds starting from:

3672 ___ ___ ___ ___ ___

5. Draw a ring around any **even** numbers you can see in this list.

34   **67**   **182**   **780**   **1653**   **2889**

6. Count on in threes from:

17 ___ ___ ___ ___ ___ ___

7. Count back in fours from:

96 ___ ___ ___ ___ ___

8. Write any five multiples of:

a) 3 ___ ___ ___ ___ ___   b) 4 ___ ___ ___ ___ ___

9. Fill in the missing numbers in these sequences.

a)

| | | 36 | | | 60 | | |

b)

| | 112 | | | | | 47 | |

Counting on and back beyond zero

We can continue this sequence **4**, **3**, **2**, **1**, **0** by counting back past zero.

5,   4,   3,   2,   1,   0,   –1,   –2,   –3,   –4,   –5,   –6...

Look at the numbers in purple. Each number is one less than the number to its left.

Look at the numbers in black. The same thing happens. Each number is one less than the number to its left.

Counting back beyond zero

1. Continue these sequences.

a) 9   8   7   6 _____ _____ _____ _____ _____ _____

b) 4   3   2   1 _____ _____ _____ _____ _____ _____

c) 0   –1   –2   –3 _____ _____ _____ _____ _____ _____

d) –7 –8 –9 –10 _____ _____ _____ _____ _____ _____

Counting on beyond zero

2. Continue these sequences.

a) –1   0   1   2 _____ _____ _____ _____ _____ _____

b) –4   –3   –2   –1 _____ _____ _____ _____ _____ _____

c) –10 –9 –8 –7 _____ _____ _____ _____ _____ _____

d) –15 –14 –13 –12 _____ _____ _____ _____ _____ _____

3. Fill in the gaps in these sequences.

a) (4)(3)( )( )( )(–1)( )( )

b) ( )( )(–2)( )( )( )(–6)(–7)

c) (–9)(–10)( )( )( )( )(–15)( )

Explaining number sequences

If you are asked to continue and explain a number sequence:

- Look at the **difference** between the numbers – write a 'line of differences'.

- Use words like 'difference', 'larger', 'smaller', 'decreasing', 'increasing'...

1. *Explain this pattern*

6   15   24   33   42   ... →

line of differences ——→ 9   9   9   9

> The numbers in this sequence get larger by a difference of **9** each time.

2. *Explain this pattern*

7   8   10   13   17   ... →

line of differences ——→ 1   2   3   4

> The difference between each number in this sequence increases by **1** each time.

1. Continue each sequence and then explain it.

a)

26   19   12

a) _____
_____
_____

b)

33   18   3

b) _____
_____
_____

c)

1   3   6   10

c) _____
_____
_____

d)

27   39   51

d) _____
_____
_____

e)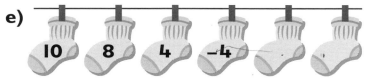

10   8   4   −4

e) _____
_____
_____

Predicting numbers in a sequence

When looking at sequences, you can predict whether a large number will be in the sequence if you carried it on.

This sequence produces multiples of **4**: **4, 8, 12, 16, 20, 24, 28...**

*Will **401** be in this sequence or not?*
It will not, as **401** is not a multiple of **4**

This sequence produces numbers that
are one more than the multiples of **4**: **5, 9, 13, 17, 21, 25, 29...**

*Will **401** be in this sequence or not?*
401 will be in this sequence as it is one more than a multiple of **4**

Look for other patterns too, like whether the numbers in the sequence are all odd, or all even or whether the unit digit is always **6** and so on.

1. Predict whether the number in the box is in each sequence. Circle yes or no.

a) 5, 10, 15, 20, 25, 30, 35...   **500**   yes / no

b) 6, 12, 18, 24, 30, 36...   **81**   yes / no

c) 22, 27, 32, 37, 42, 47...   **73**   yes / no

d) 48, 58, 68, 78, 88, 98...   **358**   yes / no

e) 7, 15, 23, 31, 39, 47...   **87**   yes / no

f) 14, 21, 28, 35, 42, 49...   **707**   yes / no

g) 15, 26, 37, 48, 59, 70...   **124**   yes / no

h) 26, 51, 76, 101, 126, 151...   **306**   yes / no

i) 4, 7, 10, 13, 16, 19, 22...   **302**   yes / no

j) 29, 59, 89, 119, 149...   **299**   yes / no

k) 24, 36, 48, 60, 72, 84...   **132**   yes / no

Did you know...? Decimal numbers, like fractions, are called 'part' numbers because they are not whole numbers. They lie **between** whole numbers.
For example **2·5** lies between **3** and **4**, and **5·25** lies **between 5** and **6**.

Decimals on number lines

We can put decimals onto number lines to show where they lie.

This number line is marked in quarters and halves:

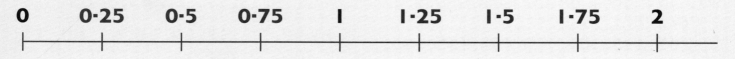

| 0 | 0·25 | 0·5 | 0·75 | 1 | 1·25 | 1·5 | 1·75 | 2 |

This number line is marked in fifths:

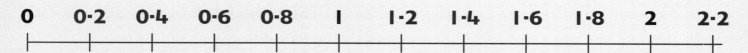

| 0 | 0·2 | 0·4 | 0·6 | 0·8 | 1 | 1·2 | 1·4 | 1·6 | 1·8 | 2 | 2·2 |

Drawing number lines can sometimes help us to count on or back in decimals.

1. Complete these sequences.

a) 0·7   0·8   0·9

b) 1·6   1·8   2·0

c) 1·25   1·5   1·75

d) 0·5   1·0   1·5

2. Count on in steps of **0·25** from **0·3**

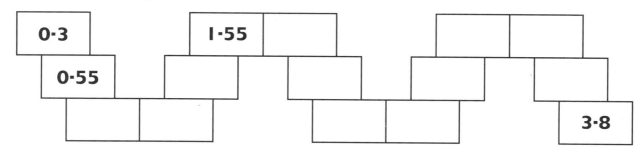

0·3   0·55   1·55   3·8

Answers to Activities

Page 4

1. a) 60, 70, 80, 90, 100, 110, 120, 130, 140, 150, 160, 170
   b) 93, 103, 113, 123, 133, 143, 153, 163, 173, 183, 193, 203
2. a) 152, 142, 132, 122, 112, 102, 92, 82, 72, 62, 52, 42
   b) 218, 208, 198, 188, 178, 168, 158, 148, 138, 128, 118, 108
3. a) 37, 47, 57, 67, 77, 87, 97, 107, 117, 127
   b) 73, 83, 93, 103, 113, 123, 133, 143, 153, 163
   c) 205, 195, 185, 175, 165, 155, 145, 135, 125, 115
   d) 388, 378, 368, 358, 348, 338, 328, 318, 308, 298

Page 5

1. a) 300, 400, 500, 600, 700, 800, 900, 1000, 1100, 1200
   b) 853, 953, 1053, 1153, 1253, 1353, 1453, 1553, 1653, 1753
   c) 1542, 1642, 1742, 1842, 1942, 2042, 2142, 2242, 2342, 2442
2. a) 1400, 1300, 1200, 1100, 1000, 900, 800, 700, 600, 500
   b) 3782, 3682, 3582, 3482, 3382, 3282, 3182, 3082, 2982, 2882
   c) 7861, 7761, 7661, 7561, 7461, 7361, 7261, 7161, 7061, 6961
3. a) 1000, 1100, 1200, 1300, 1400, 1500, 1600, 1700, 1800, 1900
   b) 6217, 6317, 6417, 6517, 6617, 6717, 6817, 6917, 7017, 7117
   c) 5442, 5342, 5242, 5142, 5042, 4942, 4842, 4742, 4642, 4542
   d) 7851, 7751, 7651, 7551, 7451, 7351, 7251, 7151, 7051, 6951
   e) 8436, 8536, 8636, 8736, 8836, 8936, 9036, 9136, 9236, 9336

Page 6

1. 56, 78, 814
2. 99, 175, 681
3. a) any three consecutive numbers starting with an even number.
   b) 3 odd numbers added together.
   c) 2 even numbers, and 2 odd numbers subtracted.
   d) 2 even numbers multiplied together.

Page 7

1. a) 7, 10, 13, 16, 19, 22, 25, 28, 31, 34, 37
   b) 58, 55, 52, 49, 46, 43, 40, 37, 34, 31, 28
2. a) 7, 11, 15, 19, 23, 27, 31, 35, 39, 43, 47
   b) 58, 54, 50, 46, 42, 38, 34, 30, 26, 22, 18
3. a) 9, 14, 19, 24, 29, 34, 39, 44, 49, 54, 59
   a) 83, 78, 73, 68, 63, 58, 53, 48, 43, 38, 33

Page 8

1. a) any five even numbers
   b) any five multiples of **3**
   c) any five multiples of **5**
   d) any five multiples of **8**
   e) any five multiples of **50**
   f) any five multiples of **100**
2. a) 44, 12, 6, 60, 100, 38, 94
   b) 42, 63, 15, 18, 39, 12, 9, 27
   c) 44, 12, 60, 100
   d) 25, 15, 40
3.

Answers to Activities

Page 9
1.
a) 9, 13, 17, 21, 25, 29
b) 12, 17, 22, 27, 32, 37
c) 17, 23, 29, 35, 41, 47
d) 19, 26, 33, 40, 47, 54
e) 154, 143, 132, 121, 110, 99
f) 207, 195, 183, 171, 159, 147
2.
a) 37, 41, 45, 49, 53, 57, 61, 65
b) 80, 73, 66, 59, 52, 45, 38, 31
c) 38, 59, 80, 101, 122, 143, 164, 185

Page 11
1.
a) ... 5, 4, 3, 2, 1, 0, −1
b) ... 0, −1, −2, −3, −4, −5, −6
c) ... −4, −5, −6, −7, −8, −9, −10
d) ... −11, −12, −13, −14, −15, −16, −17
2.
a) ... 3, 4, 5, 6, 7, 8, 9
b) ... 0, 1, 2, 3, 4, 5, 6
c) ... −6, −5, −4, −3, −2, −1, 0
d) ... −11, −10, −9, −8, −7, −6, −5
3.
a) 4, 3, 2, 1, 0, −1, −2, −3
b) 0, −1, −2, −3, −4, −5, −6, −7
c) −9, −10, −11, −12, −13, −14, −15, −16

Page 12
1.
a) 5, −2, −9
   The decreasing sequence starts with 26. The difference is 7 each time.
b) −12, −27, −42
   The decreasing sequence starts with 33. The difference is 15 each time.
c) 15, 21
   The increasing sequence starts with 1. The difference increases by one each time, e.g. 2, 3, 4, 5...
d) 63, 75, 87
   The increasing sequence starts with 27. The difference is 12 each time.
e) −20, −52
   The decreasing sequence starts with 10. The difference doubles each time, starting with 2, e.g. 2, 4, 8...

Page 13
1.
a) yes   b) no   c) no   d) yes
e) yes   f) yes   g) no   h) no
i) no   j) yes   k) yes

Page 14
1.
a) ...1·0, 1·1, 1·2, 1·3, 1·4, 1·5, 1·6
b) ...2·2, 2·4, 2·6, 2·8, 3·0, 3·2, 3·4
c) ...2·0, 2·25, 2·5, 2·75, 3·0, 3·25, 3·5
d) ...2·0, 2·5, 3·0, 3·5, 4·0, 4·5, 5·0
2.
0·3, 0·55, 0·8, 1·05, 1·3, 1·55, 1·8, 2·05, 2·3, 2·55, 2·8, 3·05, 3·3, 3·55, 3·8

Page 15
1.
a) any five multiples of 6
b) any five multiples of 7
c) any five multiples of 8
d) any five multiples of 9
2.
a) 18, 48, 60, 6, 90, 84
b) 42, 56, 70, 63, 35, 105
c) 88, 24, 40, 16, 72
d) 27, 45, 63, 54, 36, 72, 90, 99
3.

48   100   36   40

72   16   84   120

63   56   35   60

90   42   98   45

78   168   96

Page 16
1. $4^2 = 4 \times 4 = 16$
   $6^2 = 6 \times 6 = 36$
   $7^2 = 7 \times 7 = 49$
   $8^2 = 8 \times 8 = 64$
   $9^2 = 9 \times 9 = 81$
   $11^2 = 11 \times 11 = 121$
   $12^2 = 12 \times 12 = 144$
2.
a) 5cm   b) 10cm   c) 9cm   d) 11cm

Answers to Activities

Page 18
1. 1, 2, 3, 4, 6, 8, 12, 24
2. 1, 2, 3, 4, 6, 9, 12, 18, 36
3. 1, 2, 3, 4, 5, 6, 10, 12, 15, 20, 30, 60

Page 19
1. a) 1, 2, 3, 5, 6, 10, 15, 30
   b) 1, 2, 4, 8, 16, 32
   c) 1, 2, 3, 4, 6, 8, 9, 12, 18, 24, 36, 72
   d) 1, 2, 3, 4, 6, 8, 12, 16, 24, 32, 48, 96

Page 20
1. 2, 3, 5, 7, 11, 13, 17, 19, 23, 29, 31, 37, 41, 43, 47, 53, 59, 61, 67, 71, 73, 79, 83, 89, 97

Page 21
1. a) 1×12, 3×4
   b) 1×20, 2×10, 4×5
   c) 1×42, 2×21, 7×6, 3×14
2. a) 2, 3
   b) 2, 5
   c) 2, 3, 7
3. a) $2 \times 2 \times 2$
   b) $2 \times 2 \times 2 \times 2$
   c) $2 \times 2 \times 2 \times 3$
   d) $2 \times 2 \times 2 \times 2 \times 2$
   e) $2 \times 2 \times 3 \times 3$
   f) $2 \times 2 \times 2 \times 5$
   g) $2 \times 2 \times 3 \times 5$
   h) $3 \times 3 \times 3$
   i) $2 \times 2 \times 2 \times 2 \times 2 \times 3$

Page 22
1. 3, 6, 9, 12, ⑮, 18, 21, 24, 27, ㉚
   5, 10, ⑮, 20, 25, ㉚, 35, 40, 45, 50
2. 4, 8, ⑫, 16, 20, ㉔, 28, 32, ㊱, 40
   6, ⑫, 18, ㉔, 30, ㊱, 42, 48, 54, 60
3. a) 12   b) 6   c) 24
   d) 18   e) 42   f) 6

Page 23
1. a) Multiply the number of days by **24**
   b) Multiply the number of years by **12**
   c) Multiply £**6** by the number of CDs and subtract the answer from **50**

Page 24
1. a) Number of centimetres = $100n$
   b) Number of weeks = $52n$
   c) Price in pounds = $11n$

Page 25
1. a) $c - 4$
   b) $9 + c$
   c) $2c$
   d) $c + 4$
   e) $\frac{1}{2} c$
   f) $8 + c$

Answers to Tests

PROGRESS TEST 1 – Page 10
1. 78, 88, 98, 108, 118, 128, 138, 148, 158, 168, 178, 188
2. 166, 156, 146, 136, 126, 116, 106, 96, 86, 76
3. 294, 394, 494, 594, 694, 794, 894, 994, 1094, 1194
4. 3672, 3572, 3472, 3372, 3272, 3172, 3072, 2972, 2872, 2772
5. 34, 182, 780 (1 mark each)
6. 17, 20, 23, 26, 29, 32, 35, 38, 41, 44, 47
7. 96, 92, 88, 84, 80, 76, 72, 68, 64, 60, 56
8. a) any five multiples of **3** (1 mark each)
   b) any five multiples of **4** (1 mark each)
9. a) 20, 28, 36, 44, 52, 60, 68, 76
   b) 125, 112, 99, 86, 73, 60, 47, 34

Total marks = 21

PROGRESS TEST 2 – Page 17
1. a) ... 1, 0, –1, –2, –3, –4, –5
   b) ... –10, –11, –12, –13, –14, –15, –16
2. 2, 1, 0, –1, –2, –3, –4, –5
3. ... –1, –13, –25
   This decreasing sequence starts on **35** and has a difference of **12** each time.
4. a) no   b) yes
5. 0·7, 0·9, 1·1, 1·3, 1·5, 1·7, 1·9, 2·1, 2·3, 2·5, 2·7, 2·9, 3·1, 3·3, 3·5
6. (1 mark each)

 56   92   108   48   45

 63   60   110   84   128

7. (1 mark each)
   ... 9, 16, 25, 36, 49, 64, 81, 100

Total marks = 26

FINAL TEST – Pages 26 to 28
1. 176, 166, 156, 146, 136, 126, 116, 106, 96, 86, 76
2. 2435, 2335, 2235, 2135, 2035, 1935, 1835, 1735, 1635
3. 53, 535, 1041, 2309 (1 mark each)
4. 72, 67, 62, 57, 52, 47, 42, 37, 32, 27, 22
5. a) 140, 121, 102, 83, 64, 45, 26, 7
   b) 8, 15, 22, 29, 36, 43, 50, 57
6. a) 0, –1, –2, –3, –4, –5, –6, –7
   b) 21, 15, 9, 3, –3, –9, –15, –21
7. 3.3, 3.8, 4.3, 4.8, 5.3, 5.8, 6.3
8. a) yes   b) no
9. a) any five multiples of **6** (1 mark each)
   b) any five multiples of **7** (1 mark each)
   c) any five multiples of **8** (1 mark each)
   d) any five multiples of **9** (1 mark each)
10. a) 49   b) 64   c) 81
11. a) 1, 2, 3, 4, 6, 9, 12, 18, 36
    b) 1, 2, 3, 4, 6, 8, 12, 16, 24, 48
    c) 1, 2, 4, 5, 10, 20, 25, 50, 100
12. any **6** prime numbers – check against the list on page 20. (1 mark each)
13. a) $2 \times 3 \times 5$ b) $2 \times 2 \times 7$
    c) $2 \times 2 \times 2 \times 3 \times 3$
14. a) 8   b) 36   c) 24
15. Multiply the number of days by **24**
16. cost = 4n
17. a) y – 1
    b) 2b
    c) 25 – d

Total marks = 57

1. Write any five multiples of:

a) **6** ____ ____ ____ ____ ____   b) **7** ____ ____ ____ ____ ____

c) **8** ____ ____ ____ ____ ____   d) **9** ____ ____ ____ ____ ____

2. Draw a ring around the numbers that are:

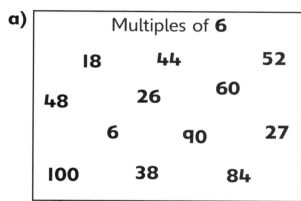

a)
Multiples of **6**

18   44   52

48   26   60

6   90   27

100   38   84

b)
Multiples of **7**

27   37   35

42   53   63

56   40   29

70   107   105

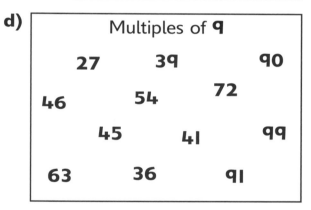

c)
Multiples of **8**

34   40   72

46   58   16

24   50   100

88   38   92

d)
Multiples of **9**

27   39   90

46   54   72

45   41   99

63   36   91

3. Use the key to draw the correct shapes around the numbers.

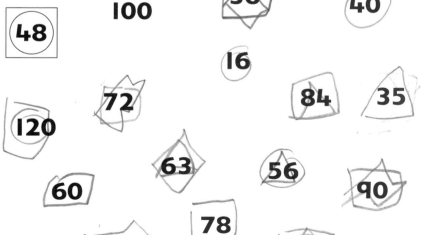

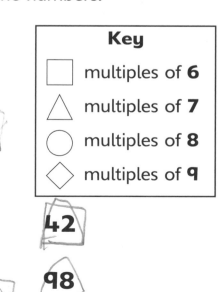

100   36   40

48   16

120   72   84   35

63   56   90   42

60   78

45   168   96   98

Key

☐ multiples of **6**
△ multiples of **7**
○ multiples of **8**
◇ multiples of **9**

Square numbers

Square numbers are called square because they can be drawn as squares.

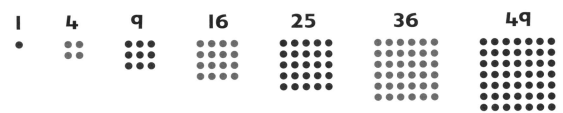

Square numbers are the result of multiplying a number by itself, like this:

$1 \times 1 = 1$, $2 \times 2 = 4$, $8 \times 8 = 64$, $10 \times 10 = 100$, $200 \times 200 = 40\,000$

We use a small, raised ^{2} to mean squared, like this:

3^2 means **3** squared, or 3×3, which equals **9**, $5^2 = 5 \times 5 = 25$ and $10^2 = 10 \times 10 = 100$

1. Join any tickets that show the same amount.

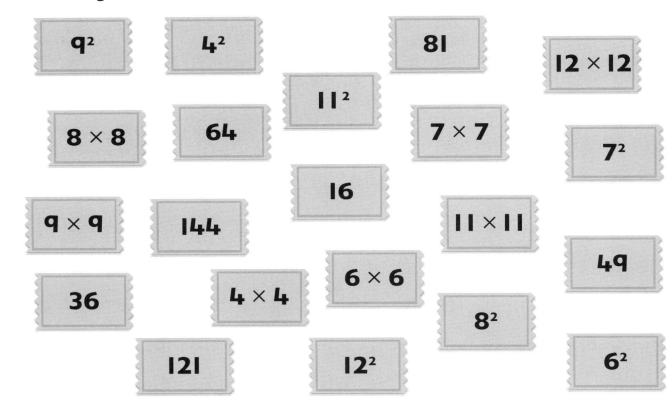

9^2	4^2	81	12×12
8×8	64	11^2	7×7
		16	7^2
9×9	144	11×11	
36	4×4	6×6	49
		8^2	
121	12^2		6^2

2. Find the lengths of the sides of these squares.

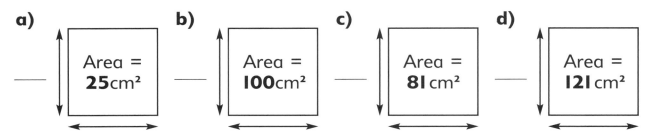

a) Area = **25**cm²

b) Area = **100**cm²

c) Area = **81** cm²

d) Area = **121** cm²

Progress Test 2

 1. Continue these sequences.

    a) 5   4   3   2 ____ ____ ____ ____

    b) –6 –7 –8 –9 ____ ____ ____ ____

 2. Fill in the gaps in this sequence.

 3. Continue the sequence and then explain it.

35   23   11

_____

_____

_____

 4. Predict whether the number in the box is in each sequence. Circle yes or no.

    a)   8, 16, 24, 32, 40, 48, 56...   **482**   yes / no

    b)   6, 13, 20, 27, 34, 41, 48...   **699**   yes / no

 5. Count on in steps of **0·2** from **0·7**

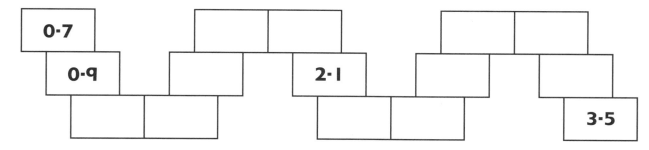

 6. Use the key to draw the correct shapes around the numbers.

56   48   45

  92   108

         84

63   128

  60   110

Key	
☐	multiples of **6**
△	multiples of **7**
○	multiples of **8**
◇	multiples of **9**

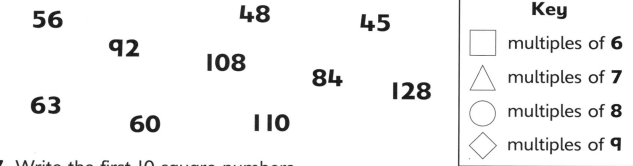

 7. Write the first 10 square numbers.

   1   4 ____ ____ ____ ____ ____

Did you know...? A **factor** is a whole number that divides **exactly** into another number. The factors of **12** are **1**, **2**, **3**, **4**, **6** and **12**, because each of these numbers divides exactly into **12**.

Look for factors by finding pairs of numbers that multiply to make your number, like this:
Find the factors of 12   1 × 12,   2 × 6,   3 × 4

1. Write the lengths of the sides of these rectangles. Use your answers to write all the factors of **24**

3cm | Area = 24cm² |
—— cm

—— cm | Area = 24cm²
12cm

1cm | Area = 24cm² |
—— cm

4cm | Area = 24cm² |
—— cm

factors of **24** _____

2. Write what the lengths of the sides of these rectangles might be, and list the factors of **36**

—— cm | Area = 36cm² | —— cm
—— cm

Area = 36cm² | —— cm | Area = 36cm²
—— cm | —— cm

—— cm | Area = 36cm²
—— cm | —— cm | Area = 36cm²
—— cm

factors of **36** _____

3. Write **all** the factors of **60**. Draw rectangles to help you.

factors of **60** _____

Finding factors 2

Checking you have all the factors

How do you know whether you have found all the factors of a number? Here's one way:

Find all the factors of **48**

Start with **1** and its partner that multiplies to **48**

Now try **2**

Try **3**

Try **4**

Try **5**

Try **6**

Try **7**

Try **8**

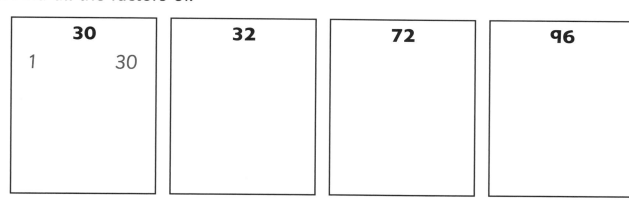

48	
1	48
2	24
3	16
4	12
5̶	5 is not a factor of **48**
6	8
7̶	7 is not a factor of **48**
8	

We already know 8 is a factor, so, when we have 'turned the corner' we know we have found all the factors.

So, the factors of **48** are **1, 2, 3, 4, 6, 8, 12, 16, 24, 48**

1. Find all the factors of:

30		32	72	96
1	30			

Write the factors of each number in a list.

a) the factors of **30** are _____

b) the factors of **32** are _____

c) the factors of **72** are _____

d) the factors of **96** are _____

Recognising prime numbers

Prime numbers are numbers that only have **two** factors, the number itself and 1.

These numbers are all prime numbers:

	factors			factors
2	1 and 2		13	1 and 13
3	1 and 3		29	1 and 29
11	1 and 11		43	1 and 43

Note that 1 isn't a prime number because it only has one factor.

1. Follow each instruction and colour the squares you land on.
Don't colour the squares you start on.

- Start on **2**
  Count in twos

- Start on **3**
  Count in threes

- Start on **4**
  Count in fours

- Start on **5**
  Count in fives

- Start on **6**
  Count in sixes

- Start on **7**
  Count in sevens

- Start on **8**
  Count in eights

- Start on **9**
  Count in nines

- Start on **10**
  Count in tens

1	2	3	4	5	6	7	8	9	10
11	12	13	14	15	16	17	18	19	20
21	22	23	24	25	26	27	28	29	30
31	32	33	34	35	36	37	38	39	40
41	42	43	44	45	46	47	48	49	50
51	52	53	54	55	56	57	58	59	60
61	62	63	64	65	66	67	68	69	70
71	72	73	74	75	76	77	78	79	80
81	82	83	84	85	86	87	88	89	90
91	92	93	94	95	96	97	98	99	100

You should have **25** numbers that have **not** been coloured. Write them here.

_____

_____

These are the **25** prime numbers that lie between **1** and **100**

Factorising numbers into prime factors

On pages **18** and **19** we learnt about finding **factors**, and on page **20** we found out about **prime numbers**. Let's bring these two ideas together.

1. Write pairs of factors of the trunk number on the leaves of the factor trees.

2. For each of the numbers in the tree trunks above, write down any factors that are prime numbers.

    a) 12 __2,_____   b) 20 _____   c) 42 _____

Did you know...?

The **prime factors** of **12** are **2**, **2** and **3** because **2 × 2 × 3 = 12** and **2** and **3** are prime numbers.

In the same way, the **prime factors** of **20** are **2**, **2** and **5** because **2 × 2 × 5 = 20** and **2** and **5** are prime numbers.

The **prime factors** of **42** are **2**, **3** and **7** because **2 × 3 × 7 = 42**.

When we write prime factors we:

• use prime numbers only

• sometimes use the same prime number more than once.

3. Write the prime factors of these numbers as multiplication questions.

    a) 8 __2 × 2 × 2__   b) 16 _____   c) 24 _____

    d) 32 _____   e) 36 _____   f) 40 _____

    g) 60 _____   h) 27 _____   i) 96 _____

Finding common multiples

Do you remember on page **8** we learnt that a **multiple** is a number that is in a times table?

Multiples of **4** are **4, 8, 12, 16, 20, 24, 28, 32, 36, 40, 44, ...** and they carry on in fours. Multiples of **10** go up in tens and include **50, 60, 230** and **1690**.

Numbers often have some of the same multiples as other numbers:

Multiples of **3**:   **3**   **6**   **9**   **12**   **15**   **18**   **21**   **24** ...

Multiples of **4**:   **4**   **8**   **12**   **16**   **20**   **24** ...

We say that **12** and **24** are **common multiples** of **3** and **4**, because **3** and **4** have those multiples in common.

1. Write the first ten multiples of **3** and **5**. Draw a ring around any common multiples.

3 _____

5 _____

2. Write the first ten multiples of **4** and **6**. Draw a ring around any common multiples.

4 _____

6 _____

Look at the common multiples of **3** and **5** above. The **smallest (or lowest) common multiple** of **3** and **5** is **15** because **15** is the smallest, or lowest, number that is a multiple of both **3** and **5**. The smallest (or lowest) common multiple of **4** and **6** is **12**.

3. Write the smallest common multiple of:

a) 3 and **4** _____   **b) 3** and **6** _____   **c) 8** and **12** _____

d) 6 and **9** _____   **e) 7** and **6** _____   **f) 2, 3** and **6** _____

Explaining a formula in words

These questions are all similar. They can all be solved in a similar way.

| How many days are there in 6 weeks? | How many days are there in 31 weeks? | How many days are there in 324 weeks? |

6 × 7 = 42 days   **31 × 7 = 217** days   **324 × 7 = 2268** days

Each question can be solved by **multiplying the number of weeks by 7**, because there are **7** days in a week.

1. These questions are all similar. Explain in words how you could solve them.

a)

How many hours are there in **5** days?

How many hours are there in **25** days?

How many hours are there in **105** days?

_____

_____

b)

How many months are there in **9** years?

How many months are there in **25** years?

How many months are there in **150** years?

_____

_____

c)

How much change will I get from £**50** if I buy **3** CDs costing £**6** each?

How much change will I get from £**50** if I buy **5** CDs costing £**6** each?

How much change will I get from £**50** if I buy **7** CDs costing £**6** each?

_____

_____

Explaining a formula using letters as symbols

These questions are all similar. They can all be solved in a similar way.

| How many days are there in **8** weeks? | How many days are there in **27** weeks? | How many days are there in **371** weeks? |

A formula can be used to answer any question of this type.

A **formula** is a quick way of writing a mathematical rule, like these:

| Number of days = **7** × ***n*** | or | Number of days = **7*n*** |

n **is a code that stands for the number of weeks.**

To answer the questions we swap ***n*** for the number of weeks given.
This is called **substituting**.

| Number of days = **7** × ***n***
= **7** × **8**
= **56** | Number of days = **7** × ***n***
= **7** × **27**
= **189** | Number of days = **7** × ***n***
= **7** × **371**
= **2597** |

1. These questions are all similar. Write a formula to show how you could solve them.

a)

| How many centimetres are there in **8** metres? | How many centimetres are there in **37** metres? | How many centimetres are there in **96** metres? |

b)

| How many weeks are there in **4** years? | How many weeks are there in **9** years? | How many weeks are there in **16** years? |

c)

| CDs cost £**11** each. How much will **7** CDs cost? | CDs cost £**11** each. How much will **11** CDs cost? | CDs cost £**11** each. How much will **19** CDs cost? |

Simple algebra

Did you know...?

An Arabic mathematician called Al-Khuwarizmi first used the word algebra over 1000 years ago!

Algebra is a part of maths where we use **letters** to stand for **numbers**.

These **symbols** are used in place of numbers. Can you work out what each stands for?

▲ + 3 = 7   20 − ● = 8   ■ × 3 = 12   24 ÷ ◆ = 4

Algebra uses **letters** in place of numbers in the same way.

$a + 4 = 9$ $23 - b = 16$ $c \times 5 = 20$

a stands for a number. When we add **4** to *a* we get **9**. So *a* must be **5**.	*b* stands for a number. When we take *b* from **23** we get **16**. So *b* must stand for **7**.	*c* stands for a number. When we multiply *c* by **5** we get **20**. So *c* must stand for **4**.

1. Join each situation to its formula.

a) Dan has **c** pence. He spends **4** pence. How much does he have now? $\frac{1}{2} c$

b) Deepa has **9** pence. She finds **c** pence. How much does she have now? $c + 4$

c) Jess eats **c** bags of crisps. Alice eats twice as many. How many does Alice eat? $8 + c$

d) Lucy spends £**c** in the clothes shop and £**4** in the CD shop. How much does she spend? $9 + c$

e) Pete scores **c** goals. Jack scores half as many. How many goals does Jack score? $c - 4$

f) Greg earns £**8** in the morning and £**c** in the afternoon. How much does he earn in total? $2c$

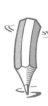

1. Count back in tens starting from:

176 _____ _____ _____ _____ _____ _____ _____ _____

2. Count back in hundreds starting from:

2435 _____ _____ _____ _____ _____ _____ _____

3. Draw a ring around any **odd** numbers you can see in this list.

26   53   162   535   1041   2309

4. Count back in fives from:

72 _____ _____ _____ _____ _____ _____ _____ _____

5. Fill in the missing numbers in these sequences.

a) [ ] [ ] [102] [ ] [ ] [ ] [26] [ ]

b) [ ] [15] [ ] [ ] [36] [ ] [ ] [ ]

6. Fill in the gaps in these sequences.

a) (0)( )( )( )( )(−5)( )( )

b) ( )(15)( )(3)( )( )( )( )

7. Count on in steps of **0·5** from **3·3**

[3·3] [ ] [ ] [ ] [ ] [ ] [ ]

8. Predict whether the number in the box is in each sequence. Circle yes or no.

a)   24, 30, 36, 42, 48, 54...   126   yes / no

b)   10, 18, 26, 34, 42, 50...   80   yes / no

9. Write any five multiples of:

a) 6   ___ ___ ___ ___ ___   b) 7   ___ ___ ___ ___ ___

c) 8   ___ ___ ___ ___ ___   d) 9   ___ ___ ___ ___ ___

10. Answer these questions.

a) $7^2 =$ b) $8^2 =$ c) $9^2 =$

11. Find all the factors of the numbers below and write them in a list.

a)   36 _____

b)   48 _____

c)   100 _____

12. Write six prime numbers.

_____

13. Write the prime factors of these numbers as multiplication questions.

a) 30 _____   b) 28 _____   c) 72 _____

14. Write the smallest common multiple of:

a) **2** and **8** _____   **b)** **4** and **9** _____   **c)** **2**, **3** and **8** _____

15. These questions are all similar. Explain in words how you could solve them.

How many hours are there in 15 days?   *How many hours are there in 29 days?*   *How many hours are there in 179 weeks?*

_____

_____

16. These questions are all similar. Write a formula to show how you could solve them.

Cinema tickets cost £4

| How much do **6** cinema tickets cost? | How much do **17** cinema tickets cost? | How much do **93** cinema tickets cost? |

_____

17. Write formulas to match these situations.

a) Molly has **y** sweets. She gives **1** away.
How many has she now? _____

b) Jack is **b** years old. His brother Sam is twice as old.
How old is Sam? _____

c) A coat costing **£25** is reduced by **£d** in the sale.
How much does it cost now? _____